Correctional Nurse Legal Briefs

Important Information to Keep You Out of Court!

Other books by Lorry Schoenly

Quick Start for Correctional Nurses:
Is Correctional Nursing for You?

The Wizard of Oz Guide
to Correctional Nursing

Correctional Health Care
Patient Safety Handbook

The Correctional Nurse Manifesto

Essentials of Correctional Nursing

Correctional Nurse Legal Briefs

Important Information to Keep You Out of Court!

Lorry Schoenly, PhD, RN, CCHP-RN
Correctional Health Care Consultant

Enchanted Mountain Press

Published in the United States by Enchanted Mountain Press

ISBN: 978-0-9912942-5-1

Contents

Introduction

Possibly more than any other nursing specialty, correctional nursing practice is lawsuit-prone. Our patient population, already in the criminal justice system, frequently seeks legal action when they feel they have not received rightful healthcare. Nurses working in the correctional setting have all the same accountability for delivering and documenting care as those working in traditional settings, along with some unique risks and liabilities that need attention. Correctional nurses must be acutely aware of malpractice and negligence concerns along with specific constitutional and civil rights issues related to the incarcerated patient.

By reading this book you will be able to

1. List common areas of nursing malpractice as they relate to the correctional nursing specialty.

2. Differentiate malpractice legal claims from constitutional and civil rights claims in correctional health care.

3. Outline methods for delivering quality nursing care to avoid legal challenges to practice.

Professional Liability Issues

A nurse hears a man-down code called overhead while returning from providing sick call in one of the housing units. When she arrives at the scene, she sees that the inmate is sprawled out on the cell floor and appears unconscious. The housing officer tells her that the inmate is breathing, so she runs back to the medical unit to get oxygen and emergency supplies. When she reaches the medical unit, she tells another nurse to activate emergency medical services as the patient will definitely be heading to the hospital. The sick call nurse returns to the housing unit with the emergency supplies, provides standard emergency treatment and, some minutes later, assists the emergency personnel to prepare the patient for transport. Three months later she is named in a malpractice lawsuit.

As professional health care providers, nurses are held to standards of practice related to our licensure. Malpractice is claimed when a professional acts, or fails to act, to the level of their professional education and skill. This is also referred to as "professional negligence" as negligence itself is a general term for carelessness or a deviation from actions that would be taken by a reasonable person in the same situation.

Components of a Malpractice Claim

Six elements must be present in a malpractice claim to prevail. All factors must be convincingly presented for the nurse to be deemed liable in a malpractice case.

Duty owed to the patient. Nurses owe a duty of care based on licensure and role at the time of the claim. A nurse-patient relationship is established by a nurse accepting an assignment involving the patient and continues until closure of that assignment. That closure can come when the patient is handed over to another qualified individual, as in the case of infirmary care, or when the patient is released to personal self-care, as at the conclusion of a sick call episode or release from the facility. That a duty is owed in a particular circumstance is fairly easy to establish. If a nurse is in the midst of a shift and working under a job description when presented with a patient, such as in our case above, the nurse owes a duty to the patient to respond as any prudent nurse would in a similar situation.

The nature of the duty is established by the circumstances of the incident. This can be less clear and in a court case often requires the testimony of expert witnesses of similar background. These expert witnesses base their testimony on practical experience in a similar setting but also on published standards. Standards for correctional nursing practice are published by the American Nurses Association and are structured around the nursing process. Expert witnesses may also rely on accreditation standards. In correctional settings, that would be the National Commission on Correctional Health Care Standards and the American Correctional Association Standards. Although voluntary, these standards lay out indicators of quality healthcare processes that may be in question in a legal claim. There are also some states that have specific state statutes and regulations that address minimum standards of care expected in the correctional setting.

Breach of the duty owed. Once duty is established, a breach of that duty then needs to be clearly presented. The groundwork has already been laid by the expert witness(es). A breach of duty relates to action or inaction that does not meet the expected standard of care for the situation. Duty owed can be established through various, often written, sources such as:

- Standing policy, procedures and protocols

- Emergency procedures

- National guidelines and standards

Foreseeability. A successful malpractice case must also establish that the nurse should have reasonably been able to foresee that harm would come. No one has a crystal ball to see into the future and some random harm can come from nurse actions. Foreseeability establishes that the injury could have been considered and steps taken to keep the patient from harm. In our case example, a nurse was called to an emergency man-down in a housing unit and was the only healthcare staff on the scene. Patient abandonment was alleged as the nurse did not assess the patient or provide immediate care before leaving the scene. A prudent nurse, it was claimed, would have stayed with the patient, rendering care while an unlicensed staff member brought the equipment. The plaintiff's lawyer argued that the nurse should have foreseen that the patient would be harmed by her departure without any other healthcare provider left there to deliver care.

Causation. The case now moves to cause. Did the nurse's breach of established duty directly cause the injury? Causation of an injury can be multi-faceted, so narrowing down cause to the nurse's action or inaction in breach of duty may be challenging. In this case, the patient suffered a hypoxic stroke, but would the outcome have been different if the nurse had repositioned the patient and provided rescue breathing? That would be for the plaintiff's legal counsel to support through the use of medical experts with experience in a similar setting.

Injury. Physical injury must then be established. This, again, must be directly linked to the nurse's breach of duty. There are some rare exceptions here, but injury must be quantifiably physical rather than merely psychological in nature. In the case above, the nurse's abandonment must be established as the proximate cause of a physical injury to the patient. This patient was permanently disabled due to brain injury.

Damages. The final element of a malpractice allegation is that damages incurred. This infers the level of the injury to the plaintiff caused by the nurse but damages can also be ascribed in a broader manner. There are three main categories of damages sought:

1. **Special damages (out-of-pocket):** These are the primary damages of a malpractice case and are determined by actual economic loss such as lost wages, medical expenses, medications or therapy. These damages can only be claimed with proof such as receipts and bills.

2. **General damages (non-economic):** These are less quantifiable damages such as pain and suffering or emotional distress. Although receipts or bills would not be available to establish this type of damage, the plaintiff must have some evidence to support the request.

3. **Punitive damages:** Punitive damages are intended to add a punishment to the defendant. If a clinician lapse is particularly

egregious, or misconduct or tampering is discovered in the case, punitive damages may be high.

Although not part of the legal case, malpractice determinations are reportable and considered by State Licensing Boards for disciplinary action such as suspension or revocation of licensure.

In this particular case, settlement was reached before trial as so often is the case. The plaintiff was awarded a large but undisclosed settlement. Was the nurse guilty of malpractice? What do you think?

Common Areas of Nursing Malpractice Claims

A study of nursing liability claims by a major nursing malpractice insurance provider grouped common allegations by the amount of paid indemnity (money paid out by the insurance company for the case) as well as frequency of the claim type. Although this data cuts across all nursing specialties, the top categories of malpractice claims have application for correctional nurses. Let's review these as they relate to the particular perils of the correctional Nurse specialty.

Scope of Practice. Scope of practice claims brought the highest payouts. The study authors proposed that this was due to a perception by the public that practicing outside of a nurse's professional license is particularly grievous. Correctional nurses have high risk of practicing outside the scope of licensure. Our specialty practice has few boundaries. Correctional peers may have little understanding of what nurses can and cannot be asked to do. There may be pressure to limit the involvement of costly outside resources. Wanting to be helpful in a difficult situation, nurses may slip into poor practice outside licensure limits. All nurses must understand the limits of their licensure, but correctional nurses, in particular, must also be willing to speak up when asked to perform outside the boundaries.

Patient Assessment. Claims in this category are frequent. Patient assessment is a major component of correctional nursing practice, as nurses are most likely the first to see the patient, and a timely assessment indicates need for monitoring, treatment or referral to another professional such as a provider, dentist or mental health specialist. The most frequent successful claims in this category were failure to properly or fully complete a patient assessment and failure to assess the need for medical intervention. Of note is a category of claims related to failure to consider or assess the patient's expressed complaints or symptoms. Correctional nurses can easily slip into a pattern of considering patient complaints to be malingering, manipulative or attention-seeking. Yet, all patient complaints and expressed symptoms must be objectively evaluated as a part of professional nursing practice.

Patient Monitoring. Once again, correctional nurses, as the primary healthcare staff in a correctional setting, are required to monitor patient conditions and alert providers if changes warrant treatment alterations. The highest percentage of closed claims in this category was related to failure to monitor and report changes in the patient's medical or emotional condition to the practitioner.

Treatment/Care. This was a broad category in the nursing malpractice data. It included not completing orders for patient treatment as well as delays in completing orders. Mentioned in the report was the need for effective communication among practitioners as many claims were the result of communication failures. Correctional nurses often work with providers who are only minimally on-site and must be contacted by phone for orders or evaluations. Broken communication systems or delays in communication are frequent in an on-call situation. In addition, staff nurses and providers may be unfamiliar with each other, leading to judgment concerns and unfamiliarity with style and perspective. If a provider or nurse is known to be hostile or uncivil, hesitation and delay in communication can result.

Medication Administration. Drug-related errors figure prominently in this evaluation of nursing malpractice claims. The most frequent cause of medication administration claims was giving the wrong dose of medication followed by using improper technique, and administering the wrong medication. Authors of this report noted, once again, the importance of communication, particularly in clarification of confusing medication orders before administration. Medication administration in the correctional setting has additional challenges that increase risk. Pill lines are often long and nurses can be pressured to complete medication administration quickly due to other security concerns. Cell-side medication delivery in high-security areas such as administrative segregation can lead to pre-pouring medication - an increased error risk.

Documentation Deficiencies. As expected, poor documentation of nursing care contributed to many malpractice claims against nurses. Incomplete documentation was a factor in many of the above categories and bears mention as a liability risk. Correctional nurses are often called upon to maintain documentation in less-than-ideal situations. If a physical charting system is in use, the single chart may be unavailable at the time and location of care delivery. Even electronic medical records require computer availability (of a sufficient number) and accessibility (located where care is delivered). Nurses delivering care in a disseminated system may not be able to chart until returning to the medical unit hours later.

There are many legal risks to working in a correctional setting, but nurses can greatly reduce the possibility of a malpractice claim by attending to the above areas of vulnerability.

Constitutional and Civil Rights Issues

In addition to malpractice claims, nurses working in corrections must also be aware of the constitutional civil rights of detained and sentenced patients that might be abridged in nursing practice situations. A body of judgments and class action cases has grown over the last four decades with escalation following the Supreme Court decision on Estelle v. Gamble in 1976. Texas prisoner J. W. Gamble injured his back working on a prison farm. He contended he was not given medical treatment and even punished for his inability to work. His suit was against W. J. Estelle, the then director of the Texas State Department of Corrections. The case moved through the lower courts and came before the Supreme Court where it was judged a violation of the Eighth Amendment's prohibition of 'cruel and unusual punishment' to not provide necessary healthcare to prisoners. This court decision established the standard of 'deliberate indifference to serious medical needs' as a breach of the Eighth Amendment of the US Constitution.

Deliberate Indifference Explained

Inmate Brown is suing the medical director and nurses at a county jail facility for not treating a leg ulcer that later developed osteomyelitis after release. He is charging deliberate indifference to his condition. While being confined to the jail for 10 days he did not mention the leg ulcer to any medical staff and left the facility before the required 14-day physical assessment. Does he have a case?

The term "deliberate indifference" seems almost an oxymoron. Can you really be deliberately indifferent to something? This created phrase, however, is in standard usage in correctional healthcare and needs to be understood as it relates to nursing practice. Deliberate indifference is defined as a professional knowing of, and disregarding, an inmate's serious medical need.

Components of deliberate indifference:

- There must be a serious medical need

- Staff must know about the serious need

- Staff must intentionally and deliberately fail to provide required treatment for that need

- This failure to treat must be shown to have caused the inmate unneeded pain or suffering or similar harm

In the case above, staff was not aware of the leg ulcer while Mr. Brown was in custody and there is no indication that staff deliberately or intentionally refused to treat his condition. It is unlikely that his case would prevail.

Serious Medical Need

According to the Supreme Court decision in Estelle v. Gamble, a serious medical need is one that, if left untreated, has a risk of serious harm to the patient and can be one of two categories:

- Diagnosed by a physician as requiring treatment

- Is a need so obvious that even a lay person would know it needed medical attention

Again, the case above does not meet either of the standards for serious medical need. Claims of this type are more common than you might think in our particular clinical specialty. Many such cases are brought by the inmate without legal counsel and are referred to as 'pro se' cases. Pro se means a plaintiff speaks on their own behalf without legal representation.

Three Basic Rights of *Estelle v. Gamble*

The precedent-setting Supreme Court case of *Estelle v. Gamble* established the basic rights of healthcare for incarcerated citizens. Many court cases over the ensuing 40 years have unpacked these rights and further described them. While reading these descriptions, consider how your nursing practice is affected by the basic principle underlying the right.

Access to Medical Care. The first provision of the Supreme Court ruling is the basic right to medical care access. If an inmate needs medical attention, this cannot be denied. There are many ways in which medical care can be passively denied. Barriers to care can be found in the structure and process of security services and healthcare delivery systems. For example, a facility may not have enough healthcare staff to meet the needs of the inmate population. If patients must wait weeks to be seen by a practitioner for an urgent condition, access to care is being hindered. This provision also covers specialists and inpatient treatment.

If the medical care needed for a condition cannot be provided by on-site staff, adequate and timely access to specialists must be provided.

Care That Was Ordered. If medical staff determine that a treatment is needed and an order for the treatment or medication is written, it must be honored. Security staff or internal processes cannot hinder the required treatment nor can treatment be countermanded. Of course, accommodation of security concern is understood to be foundational and collaboration with custody staff is needed to deliver medical care in jails and prisons. An example of abridgment of this right would be for custody staff to require an inmate to report to work duty when bed rest was ordered for treatment of a sprained ankle. What *Estelle v. Gamble* imposes, then, is a legal duty on the part of the custodial authority to honor medical orders.

A Professional Judgment. The third medical right for inmates garnered by *Estelle v. Gamble* is a right to a professional judgment. This right covers the need for appropriate healthcare staff to assess and determine medical care required by an inmate. The courts want to be sure that decisions about medical care are based on medical need and not on security need or convenience. For example, necessary care cannot be denied due to budgetary constraints or as a punishment. Healthcare staff cannot avoid a patient because he or she is a complainer or is obnoxious. Inmates, unlike free citizens, are not able to access other sources of care if they are not getting their needs met when incarcerated. The courts want to ensure that this does not adversely affect them. This right has significant implications for correctional nurses. Inmates cannot be avoided or disregarded because they are labeled as 'trouble-makers' or 'manipulators'. Treatment cannot be denied because it is too expensive for the budget. This is not to eliminate efforts to be as cost-effective as possible in providing adequate care, however.

Section 1983

Subpoenas have been issued at your jail for an inmate claim that his continuing headaches were ignored and he was denied necessary treatment of his 'serious medical need'. Your risk manager and legal counsel will be meeting with staff members involved in the case, including nurses involved in triaging the sick call slips. They are referring to this as a Section 1983 case.

When first hearing the term Section 1983, it might appear to be a reference to a date. However, 1983 is not a year but a section of the US Civil Rights Act of 1871. This act was created to protect those who were being harassed by the Ku Klux Klan following the Civil War. Section 1983 of this act is the means through which US citizens can bring forward a civil claim that their constitutionally-protected rights have been violated.

Section 1983 legal claims include false arrest, unreasonable searches, equal protection and excessive force. For correctional nursing practice, Section 1983 claims involve abridgment of the Eighth or Fourteenth Amendment to the Constitution as it relates to healthcare provision of prisoners or detainees. In *Estelle v. Gamble (1976)* the Supreme Court ruled that denial of adequate medical care constituted "cruel and unusual punishment" as was protected against by the Eighth Amendment to the Constitution. Jail detainees are not yet prisoners being 'punished' and technically are not addressed in the Eighth Amendment. However, *Bell v. Wolfish* (1979) established this same need of adequate healthcare for unconvicted detainees under the Fourteenth Amendment which protects due process for criminal conviction. In this case, the Supreme Court ruled that failure to provide medical care was a form of punishment imposed on an individual who had not been convicted of a crime. So, although unconvicted jail detainees and prison inmates have medical rights based on two different constitutional amendments, their medical care rights are essentially the same and legal claims of injustice are brought to court through Section 1983 of the Civil Rights Act.

A Section 1983 case is a civil rights case rather than a medical malpractice case and comes with a few peculiarities. Instead of looking to determine if the standard for nursing care was provided, a Section 1983 case is looking at the primary determinants of deliberate indifference to a serious medical need. Although a Section 1983 case can be tried in either a state or federal court, plaintiff lawyers with background in these cases tend to lean toward federal courts as federal judges are receptive to claims of constitutional rights violations. Section 1983 claims also have a longer shelf-life as medical malpractice claims are governed by state law and can have a shorter timeframe for filing. In addition, plaintiff attorneys like Section 1983 cases because their fees, if they prevail, must be covered by the defendant (if reasonable). This element of the law allows for the pursuit of 'smaller' claims that might not otherwise be considered.

Prison Litigation Reform Act

An inmate's wife was concerned about her husband's poor medical care while incarcerated in a state prison. She wanted to interest a legal firm in taking on the case and was wondering what information she would need to gather. A first recommendation is to take all steps necessary to remedy the situation through standard institutional channels. For example, had he already requested treatments through the normal sick call process or submitted grievances about his medical care?

The Prison Litigation Reform Act (PLRA) was passed in 1996 to require preliminary actions before a legal claim is heard by the court.

This legislation was originally proposed to limit frivolous inmate lawsuits regarding their conditions of confinement and is limited to civil cases (not medical malpractice).

Key Points of PLRA

- **Exhaustion of Administrative Remedies.** An inmate must first use the internal grievance system to the full extent (including any appeals process) before taking legal action on a claim.

- **Mental or Emotional Injury.** This injury cannot be claimed without first showing physical injury.

- **Screening and Dismissal.** PLRA allows a case to be screened by the court and dismissed as frivolous even before the defense is required to reply.

- **Three-Strikes Clause.** Upfront filing fees are generally waived or greatly decreased for inmates due to poverty. However, after three prior lawsuits dismissed as "frivolous, malicious or failing to state a claim for relief", this waiver is exhausted. Further filings will require that the full fee be paid upfront.

The number of lawsuits filed by inmates greatly increased from 1970 to 1995. More than 40,000 inmate claims clogged the legal system in 1995. The PLRA aimed to reduce frivolous and unnecessary inmate lawsuits by creating some boundaries on the types and frequency of legal claims. Lawsuits filed by inmates have been reduced to around 25,000 per year.

Confidentiality, HIPAA and the Correctional Nurse

An RN *calls the hospital for discharge information on a patient transported back to the prison infirmary from the local hospital after his jaw was wired following an inmate brawl in the exercise yard. The emergency room nurse refused to provide any information stating it would be a violation of HIPAA. She instructs the prison RN to obtain any information she needs from the patient himself.*

An NP is reprimanded for telling a housing officer that one of the inmates is a severe diabetic and needs his evening snack on time.

Confidentiality of patient health information has always been a concern for nursing. Valuing patient privacy is an ethical imperative, even in the correctional setting. In recent years, the Health Insurance Portability and Accountability Act (HIPAA) has moved healthcare information confidentiality to a legal concern for nurses. In particular, HIPAA regulations ensure that private health information is not released to any third party without the patient's permission.

Disclosure of medical information may be necessary for the health and safety of both the patient and the large patient community within a security facility. Officers may need to know about medical conditions or disabilities that require special equipment or scheduled appointments.

Some medication side effects require additional attention or changes in work duty. Joint surgery may limit movements or abilities that security needs to be aware of. Fortunately, HIPAA regulations take into account the need for some information sharing within the correctional setting and have spelled this out in the 45 C.F.R. 164.512 (k) (5) (i) section of the code. If the correctional institution represents that such protected health information is necessary for:

- The provision of healthcare to such individuals

- The health and safety of such individuals or other inmates

- The health and safety of the officers or employees or of others at the correctional institution

- The health and safety of such individuals and officers or other persons responsible for the transporting of inmates or their transfer from one institution, facility or setting to another

- Law enforcement on the premises of the correctional institution

- The administration and maintenance of the safety, security and good order of the correctional institution

According to this section of the HIPAA regulations, an emergency nurse can confidently share health information with the receiving nurse in the prison infirmary and a nurse practitioner can alert an officer to a health need of an inmate in his charge.

Ten Ways Correctional Nurses Can Land in Court

Correctional nurse experts Kathy Wild, RN, MPA, CCHP and Royanne Schissel, RN, CCHP, have decades of experience in the specialty as staff nurses, managers and legal nurse experts. They offer this advice based on the court cases they have been involved with. Remember, this is a list of what not to do!

#1 Don't listen to your patient's description of symptoms

Correctional nurses need to be good listeners. Although patients may embellish their symptoms at times, there is still truth in and among the various information bits being presented during a patient encounter. The goal is to find the important information that determines an accurate diagnosis and response. Listening also includes obtaining information from housing officers and family members. They can have important clues to what is going on. Disregard patient information at your own peril.

#2 Don't use your assessment skills when evaluating a patient complaint

Although tempting, malingering is not an appropriate nursing diagnosis. Once this thought is expressed it can set the mind of every other care provider going forward. Correctional nurses must guard against judgmentalism and, instead, gather subjective and objective data to confirm symptoms and establish causes when dealing with patient complaints.

#3 Don't call the doctor when you're not sure about something

Long-term correctional nurses can think they know more than the doctor they would be calling. Often the provider is not a corrections specialist or does not know the patient. The context of correctional nursing can allow nurses to drift into thinking they can handle almost anything without need of a physician.

#4 Don't take the time necessary to thoroughly document your encounter

Lawsuits come along years later and you won't remember the encounter without clear and thorough documentation. Document completely and thoroughly as close as you can to the patient encounter. The medical record is both a communication tool and a legal document. Be sure the record is legible, limited to the clinical facts and without commentary on what others have done. Charting should include a first-hand account of what was observed and what was performed for the patient. In addition, in our specialty, it is also necessary to document why a patient wasn't seen. For example, the patient may have been in court or released early.

#5 Not knowing what your nurse practice act says about your practice

Unlike traditional healthcare settings, nurses working in corrections may not have clear practice boundaries identified by policy, procedure, and a strong nursing organizational structure. All correctional nurses, no matter the position, must have a clear understanding of what can and cannot be done based on state licensure. Nurses can be requested to perform outside their licensure by uninformed corrections administrators, physicians and even other nurses. Just because you are able to perform a function or procedure doesn't mean that you are licensed to do it. Some nurses have a misguided impression that they must be permitted to do something since an employer requests it. This is not so.

#6 Treat your patient as an inmate

It is easy to slide into a punitive perspective in dealings with inmates. After all, some of them have learned that they can get what they want through manipulation and deceit. Yet, according to Earl Nightingale, our attitude toward others determines their attitude towards us. As nurses we are called to treat all patients with respect and dignity. We cannot disrespect or abuse the patients that we are responsible to treat.

#7 Don't share critical healthcare information with others

HIPAA release forms are not needed for every situation. We often need to share important health information with custody officers. Officers, especially housing officers, are part of the treatment team and need to be aware of significant medical conditions that may need early medical attention. Communication is important.

#8 Don't follow up on something because "It's not your job."

Nurses are responsible for positive patient outcomes. Yet, in some correctional cultures, staff are willing to do specific tasks and no more. Some correctional settings still ascribe to a functional care delivery pattern where some nurses only perform sick call while others only perform medication administration activities. "It's not my job" is not an appropriate response where patient outcomes are concerned and does not absolve nurses from responsibility in a bad outcome where something could have been done to improve a patient condition.

#9 Don't follow current protocols

Protocols often guide nursing actions in the correctional setting. They are particularly important for nursing sick call and emergency responses. Written protocols should be available at all times and staff should know where protocols can be found. For example, the only copy of clinical protocols should not be locked in a supervisor's office. Skipping protocol steps is a frequent problem in legal cases. Referring to the protocols frequently will ensure that this does not happen. Relying on memory is not good practice. Another legal concern with protocols is keeping them updated with any new changes in practice. At a minimum, nursing protocols need to be reviewed and updated annually.

#10 Don't look for other employment when you are not happy with your job

Correctional nursing is not for everyone. The environment can be unfriendly and the patient population challenging. If you don't enjoy your work you can fall into practice patterns that can land you in court. Indications that you don't like your job can include calling inmates names, calling other staff members names, having a bad attitude or taking shortcuts with patient and staff safety. Some nurses are unable to overcome concerns that inmate patients are dangerous. Yet, you can't help a patient when you are afraid. If you see these indications in yourself, consider other nursing options. Maybe correctional nursing is not a good match for you.

Summary

Most nurses are aware of basic professional liability concerns. As professionals, nurses have a duty to the public to practice within license boundaries and provide appropriate care to patients. Common areas of nursing malpractice claims are also a concern in the correctional specialty with some particular risks due to the nature of the patient and the care environment. In addition to professional liability, correctional nurses must understand the constitutional and civil rights issues surrounding providing healthcare to incarcerated individuals. The Eighth and Fourteenth Amendments to the US Constitution have been cited as foundational to the rights of sentenced and detained inmates to receive necessary healthcare. Section 1983 of the Civil Rights Act allows inmates to make a civil claim when constitutional rights are considered violated. Although correctional nurses are under the same requirements as other nurses to keep patient medical information confidential, some health information may be shared with officers if they need to be aware of a health condition in order to participate in monitoring and seeking medical treatment for those in their charge. Correctional nurses can avoid being named in court cases by being mindful to obtain objective assessments, document treatments, communicate effectively and follow established protocols.

Questions to Consider

1. What common area of nursing malpractice are you most vulnerable to in your setting?

2. Can you explain the components of deliberate indifference?

3. How have you seen these three primary medical rights of inmates implemented at your facility: access to medical care, ordered care delivered, a medical judgment provided?

4. How does Section 1983 relate to constitutional rights of inmates?

5. What medical information can you provide to correctional officers?

6. Have you been tempted or pressured to practice in any of the ten ways that could land you in court?

References

Guido, G. W. (2011). Legal and ethical issues. In P. S. Yoder-Wise (Ed.), *Leading and managing in nursing (5th ed.)*, St. Louis, MO: Elsevier Mosby.

Hoffman, P. (2009). Health care legal concepts. In R. Carroll (Ed.), Risk management handbook for health care organizations (Student ed., pp. 115-157). San Francisco, CA: Jossey-Bass.

McCarthy, D. H. (2013). Learning common categories of malpractice claims against nurses and how to reduce potential liability. ADVANCE healthcare Network. Retrieved from http://nursing.advanceweb.com/Continuing-Education/CE-Articles/Is-It-Malpractice.aspx

Moore, J. (2013). Legal considerations in correctional nursing. In L. Schoenly & C. M. Knox (Eds.),

Essentials of correctional nursing (pp. 327-348). New York, NY: Springer.

Nursing Service Organization. (2011). Understanding nursing liability, 2006-2010. A 3-part approach. Retrieved from http://www.nso.com/pdfs/db/RN-2010-CNA-Claims-Study.pdf?fileName=RN-2010-CNA-Claims-Study.pdf&folder=pdfs/db&isLiveStr=Y

Schoenly, L. (2014). *Correctional health care patient safety handbook: Reduce clinical error, manage risk, and improve quality*. Nashville, TN: Enchanted Mountain Press.

Contact Hours

CorrectionalNurse.Net is a licensed Continuing Education Provider in the State of California, CEP 16255. This educational activity is approved by the California Board of Registered Nursing (CBRN), Provider #16255, for 1 Contact Hour. CBRN Contact Hours are accepted by all State Boards of Nursing and Certifying Bodies for license renewal and recertification purposes.

To receive a Contact Hour Certificate for a $5 processing fee, go to

http://correctionalnurse.net/product/cnn1406-correctional-nurse-legal-brief-ce-certificate/

About the Author

Lorry Schoenly, PhD, RN, CCHP-RN, is a nurse author and educator specializing in the field of correctional health care. She provides consulting services to jails and prisons across the country on projects to improve professional nursing practice and patient safety. She began her corrections experience in the New Jersey Prison System where she created and implemented education for nurses, physicians, dentists, and site managers. Before "accidentally" finding correctional healthcare, she practiced in critical care and orthopaedic specialties.

Dr. Schoenly actively promotes correctional nursing through social media outlets and increases the visibility of the specialty through her popular blog – correctionalnurse.net. Her podcast, Correctional Nursing Today, reviews correctional healthcare news and interviews correctional health care leaders. She is the recipient of the "B. Jaye Anno Award of Excellence in Communication" from the National Commission on Correctional Health Care.

Made in the USA
San Bernardino, CA
09 December 2017